ROYAL
CONSERVATORY OF MUSIC

University of Toronto

ISBN 0-88797-053-2

GRADES VII & VIII
PIANOFORTE
STUDIES

The Frederick Harris Music Co. Limited

529 Speers Road, Oakville, Ontario, Canada L6K 2G4

Printed in Canada

GRADES VII and VIII

STUDIES

Contents

GRADE VII

GRADE VIII

F.H. 7878

GRADE VII
STUDY No. 1

BERTINI

STUDY No. 2

CZERNY, Op. 599, No. 64

STUDY No. 3

HOLT

Moderato circa ♩ = 96

STUDY No. 4

Allegro vivo e scherzando ♪ = 104 - 120

CZERNY, Op. 139, No. 71

pp leggiermente

Omit repeats in examinations

STUDY No. 5

CZERNY, Op. 299, No. 2

Allegro ♩ = 84 - 88

STUDY No. 6

CZERNY, Op. 139, No. 53

STUDY No. 7

CZERNY, Op. 718, No. 20

STUDY No. 8

CZERNY

STUDY No. 9

KABALEVSKY

Moderato scherzando ♩ = about 132

STUDY No. 10

CZERNY

STUDY No. 11

CZERNY, Op. 139, No. 97

STUDY No. 12

CZERNY, Op. 599, No. 69

Allegretto ♩=116

GRADE VIII
STUDY No. 1

Allegro risoluto ♩ = 104 - 126

BERENS, Op. 61, No. 4

STUDY No. 2

Andantino con tenerezza ♩=about 66

HELLER, Op. 45, No. 16

dolce   *p il accomp. leggiero*

Omit repeats in examinations

F.H. 7878

Omit repeats in examinations
F.H. 7878

STUDY No. 3

BERTINI, Op. 29, No. 8

STUDY No. 4

BERTINI

STUDY No. 5

HELLER, Op. 45, No. 15

STUDY No. 6

Allegro vivace ♩ = 108 - 132

DUVERNOY, Op. 120, No. 4

STUDY No. 7

CZERNY, Op. 299, No. 4

STUDY No. 8

BERTINI, Op. 29, No. 3

STUDY No. 9

BURGMÜLLER, Op. 109, No. 28

Allegro vivace ♩ = 112 - 126

STUDY No. 10

CZERNY, Op. 139 No. 83

STUDY No. 11

CZERNY, Op. 718, No. 10

F.H. 7878

STUDY No. 12

DUVERNOY, Op. 120, No. 6

STUDY No. 13

CZERNY, Op. 139 No. 88

STUDY No. 14

CZERNY, Op. 139, No. 68

STUDY No. 15

LAPUTIN

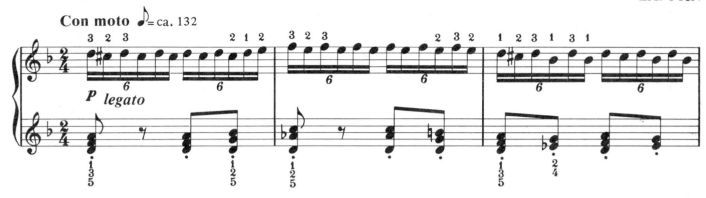

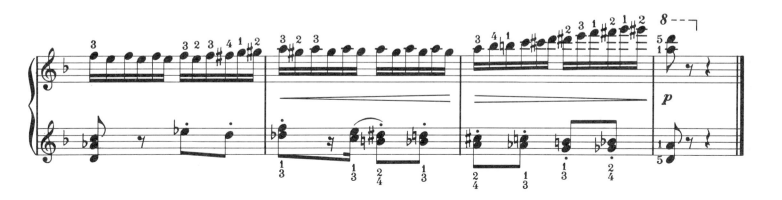

STUDY No. 16

KABALEVSKY

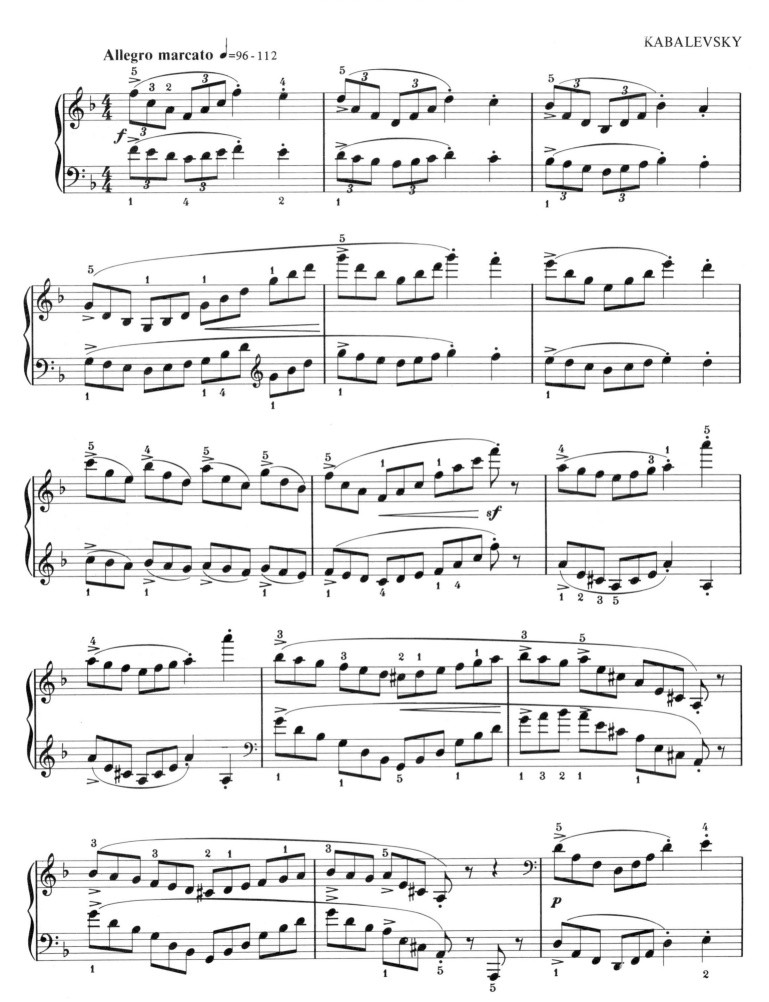

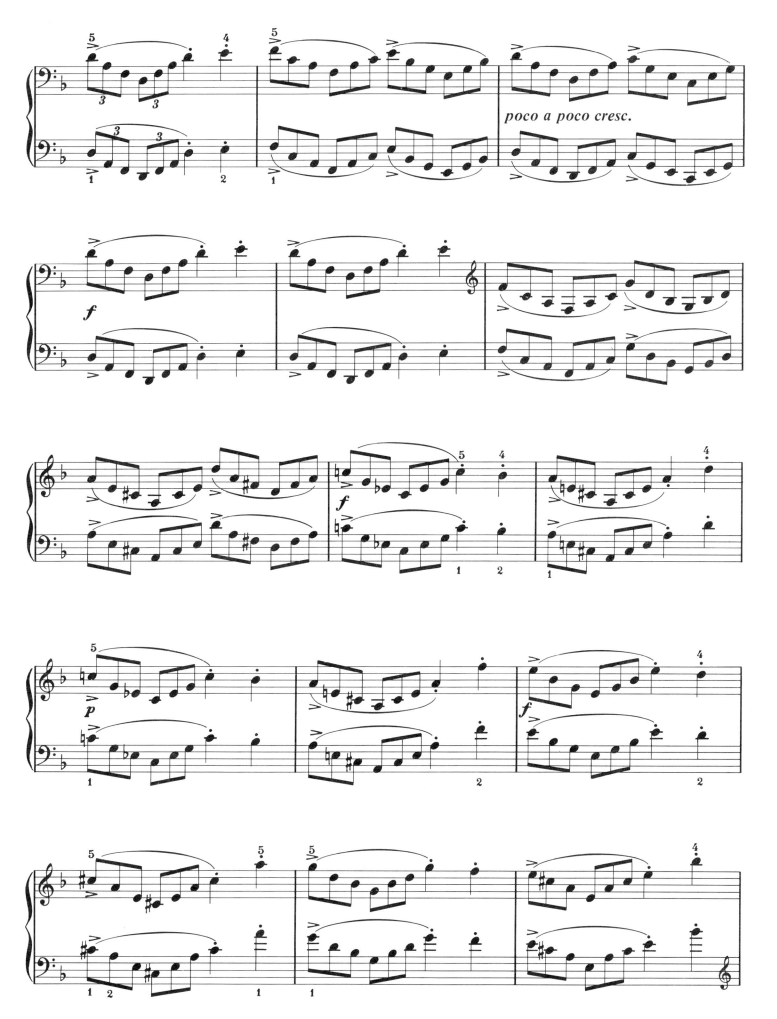

poco a poco cresc.